Fun with
AESOP
Volume II

Retold by Paul Tell   *Illustrated by* Connie Ross

Contents

For my grandson, Joey, a budding lap-listener

Many thanks to those who helped bring this new approach
to Aesop's wisdom into being, especially for Dianna Williams'
editorial direction, Connie Ross's superb illustrations, and to
Denny & Pam Adams, Bob & Suanne Crowley, Ruth Faux,
Marti Geise and Becky Snyder for their skillful manuscript
readings and suggestions, and special thanks to the children
ages four through ten who responded as wide-eyed listeners
to these stories before the pictures were ever created!

TELCRAFT ®
A division of Tell Publications
Mogadore, Ohio 44260-0053

The Goose and the Golden Eggs

There was a farmer who raised a goose. She looked like any other goose.

But when she was old enough to nest he found her first egg was bright yellow. "How beautiful," he said, as he held it up and saw it glisten in the sun.

Each day he found his goose had laid another shiny egg, and he smiled at her.

He soon discovered that these eggs were made of gold, and took them to the market where he sold his grain. People quickly bought every egg he would bring.

Then one day as the farmer was counting his money he said, "I'm getting rich, but not fast enough."

An idea came to him: If I kill the goose and open it up, I can have all the eggs at once. And I will be the richest person of all!

That was exactly what he did—he killed the goose. But when he opened her up he found no eggs! And his precious goose was gone, never to lay another egg.

What can we learn from this?

By wanting too much,
too fast,
You may do something
wrong and lose
What you have.

The Goose and the Golden Eggs

She was a wonderful goose
  and laid a golden egg
At the start
  of each new day.

The farmer was
  glad to have her,
And by selling the eggs
  he grew rich.

Now the goose was faithful, and
  every morning she'd lay
Another egg, until one afternoon
  her owner became impatient.

He thought,
  What if, instead of only
One gold egg each day,
  I get them all right now?

Well, the goose could lay
  only one new egg each day;
And the farmer lost forever
  the goose and her golden eggs.

is

A Penny Saved

A Penny Earned

Color egg gold & goose white

Instructions for Golden Egg Bank:

Copy or trace goose and egg on plain paper.
Color and cut the goose and egg on dotted lines.
Tape or paste goose and egg on to a 1 lb. coffee can. First you may want to cover the can with paper, fabric, or paint.
Cut a slit in the top of the plastic lid large enough for quarters to go through. Pennies make excellent golden eggs, but you may decide to save the larger coins also.

Try to save each day — Do not open your bank too often or you will quickly spend what you have saved.

The Fox and the Crow

One sunny morning a fox went out in search of something to eat. As he walked, his nose began to twitch at the smell of delicious cheese.

His mouth watered as he sniffed. Then he looked up. There on a tree branch he saw Sally Crow holding a piece of cheese in her beak.

My search is over, thought the fox. There is my breakfast!

He trotted up to the tree and said to the crow, "Good morning, beautiful creature!"

But Sally just stood there, cocked her head and looked. She held the cheese tightly in her beak, not wanting to drop her treat.

"How magnificant you look," said the fox. "How shiny your feathers! You must have a beautiful voice. If you would sing, I'd praise you as the Queen of Birds."

Sally soon forgot to be careful; she would very much like to be called Queen of Birds. Her mouth opened wide and she made the loudest caw a crow could make. Down fell the cheese, right into the fox's mouth!

"Thank you," said the fox.

Then as he turned to go he said, "You certainly have a strong voice, but you need to be more careful."

What does this tell us about some people who say nice things?

A person who says
something nice
may be trying to get
Something from the person
who will listen.

When a stranger says
something nice to you, it is
polite to say, "Thank you."
But be careful. This person may
be saying what he doesn't mean.

Do you know the difference
between a true *compliment* and
flattery?

8

The Fox and the Crow

Mmmmmm.
   Smell that cheese!
Where could it be,
   just waiting for me?

There it is! Way up high
   in the beak of Sally Crow.
She's so vain—certainly
   not as clever as I!

"Dear Sally,
   you look so nice today!
What have you done
   to make this morning so bright?

"Why, if you'd sing, I would
   call you Queen of Birds.
I know I'd lose my breath
   in the wonder of your voice!"

"Caaaaaaw—Caaaaaaaaw."
   There she goes!
Such a loud and crackling sound
   offends my sensitive ears!

But it's worth the noise
   for the tasty prize.
Here it comes.
   Mmm, mmm!

"Thank you, Sally.
   You are so nice
To share such treats
   with a sly old fox like me!"

I love you and I thank you for taking good care of me.

GIVE A TRUE COMPLIMENT TO SOMEONE YOU LOVE

Copy or trace "compliment cards" on to plain or parchment paper.

Color and cut out.

To add card to a gift, punch hole in corner where shown and **tie** with string or ribbon.

To:

Thank you for making my home so snug and warm.

From:

You Are *SPECIAL* To Me

YOU ARE SO SWEET

The Lion and the Mouse

One day a mouse was walking through the grass. He came upon a sleeping lion he didn't know was there.

He was so surprised that he ran over the lion's nose as he hurried to get away.

The lion awakened at the feeling of little feet upon his muzzle. He opened his eyes, and in a flash he caught the little mouse under his mighty paw.

"Oh, please, please spare me," begged the mouse. "Let me go and someday I'll repay you."

The lion laughed as he said to himself, "What could a little mouse ever do for me?" But with a feeling of kindness, he let him go.

Later the lion stood and stretched. Then, as he took a step, he heard a loud snap and suddenly was caught in a net of ropes.

No matter how hard he tried, his powerful paws could not break through. The lion became angry and roared loudly, and all the while the ropes still held him captive.

The mouse heard the lion's voice and hurried over to see him. There he was, the lion who had let him go, now caught in a hunter's net.

This is an easy problem, thought the mouse, and fun too!

He went straight to the ropes and began to chew. Soon he had gnawed through them and the lion walked out free.

"You laughed when I said I would repay you," said the mouse. "And now, you see—I have!"

What lesson can we learn?

*A kind deed is
never wasted.*

It pays to be kind:
First, because we help someone.
Then, because that person
    may some day help us,
    or someone else who needs it.

The Lion and the Mouse

This tall grass tickles
  my nose and whiskers,
And hides me
  as I go.

Oops! No! A lion!
  I must get away.
I didn't see him
  sleeping there.

Now I've done it,
  clumsy me.
I ran
  right over his nose!

Oh, no!
  I'm caught
Under his
  great soft paw!

"Dear Mr. Lion,
  King of Beasts,
Please spare me
  and I'll come back.

"I'll come and help you
  when you need it—
You won't be sorry
  you let me go."

The lion is laughing
  at such an idea.
"Do you think YOU,
  could help ME?"

He must feel
  kindly today.
He has lifted his paw;
  I'm free to go!

What's that I hear?
  It's the lion's roar!
And he doesn't sound
  very happy.

Where is he? There,
  trapped in a hunter's net.
Aha, now that's
  my specialty!

Quick—I'll gnaw the ropes
  with my sharp teeth.
See, the net just
  falls away.

"You've freed me!
  Thank you,"
Says the lion, who
  is now my friend.

Activity Page

List below jobs you can do.
Then list the jobs a grown-up needs to do for you.
Put an "x" in the box when the job is completed.

JOB LIST

Things I can do	Grown-up's jobs
☐ Set the table	☐ Cook dinner
☐ Put dirty clothes in hamper	☐ Wash clothes
☐	☐
☐	☐
☐	☐
☐	☐
☐	☐
Signed	Signed
Date	Date

We did it together!

Some grown-ups think you cannot be helpful—
but you know you can. Now think about a person
younger than you, who can also be helpful.

The Fox Without a Tail

One day a fox caught his tail in the jaws of a steel trap. He tugged and tugged and finally got away. But he had to leave his beautiful tail in the trap.

For many days the fox stayed in hiding. He was too ashamed to let the other foxes see him. He didn't want them to laugh and make fun because he had no tail. Besides, he had been so proud of his tail and liked to show it off.

Then the fox thought of a plan. He called the other foxes to a meeting. He said he had something important to tell them.

When the foxes had come together, he sat up and made a long speech. He talked about foxes who came to serious misfortune because of the problem of having a tail.

He told of a fox who couldn't outrun pursuing hounds because *the weight of his tail slowed him down.* He told about another fox who was caught by hounds when *his tail got caught in a bush.*

He ended his examples by saying that *people hunt foxes mainly for their tails* which they cut off as prizes after the hunt.

The fox thought he had given proof that tails are dangerous and useless. He finished his great speech telling the other foxes that it would be best for them to cut off their tails immediately if they believed in life and safety.

As the foxes looked at each other to see what others were thinking, a wise old fox stood up and said, "You speak very well, but turn around and you'll find your answer behind you."

The fox without a tail turned around and suddenly the other foxes began to laugh. Then he knew there was nothing he could say that would convince them to cut off their tails.

If you were one of the foxes in the meeting, and you still had your tail, what could you learn from the wise old fox?

*Do not listen to advice
from someone who wants
to bring you down
to where he is.*

Foxes are sly indeed. Here was a fox with a problem—he had no tail.

He was clever enough to think of fine-sounding reasons why the others also should not have tails.

But they were clever foxes too, and there were many of them at the meeting. Their tails were safe because of the wisdom of the old fox.

The Fox Without a Tail

How embarrassing
   for a fox like me
To walk around
   without a tail!

I want to hide
   but I can't
Stay out of sight
   forever.

I must go back
   to be with my friends;
But how can I
   without a tail?

Now, I'm a fox—I'm smart.
   I'm very smart.
And I've just thought
   of a plan.

"Friend foxes,
   don't you see
The trouble your tails
   might bring?"

"Ho, ho, turn around,"
   says a wise old fox,
"Your answer
   is behind you."

Well, at least I tried,
   but I cannot fool them.
How can a fox
   outsmart a fox?

17

Pin the Tail Back on the Fox

Copy or trace, and color fox and tails above. Make one tail for each player.

Cut out fox and tails.

Attach fox to bulletin board using tape or thumb tacks.

Play the game like Pin the Tail on the Donkey, blindfolding each player and taking turns. The tails are marked with letters to help the players remember which tail is theirs. The game is over after everyone has had a chance to play. The winner is the person who puts the pin (or tack) in the tail closest to the X on the fox where the tail should go.

Alternative ideas: Enlarge the design for a wall-size game. Also, before taking a turn, have each player tell a reason why the fox needs his tail.

The Gnat and the Bull

One hot day a gnat was flying over a meadow. He made a loud buzzing sound for so small a creature.

The gnat began to feel tired. As he looked around for a place to rest, he saw a bull eating grass. He flew over and landed on the tip of one of the bull's horns.

When he was ready to leave, he said, "Mr. Bull, please pardon me for resting on your horn. You must be happy to see me go."

"It doesn't matter to me," said the bull. "I didn't notice you were there."

What can we learn from this story about the gnat and the bull?

*We sometimes think
we are more important
than others think we are.*

SOMETIMES *we think we are
more important than we are.*

THEN *sometimes we don't feel
as important as we should.*

BUT *we are all important and
worthy of respect.*

20

The Gnat and the Bull

I'm such a fine gnat
   in great flying form.
I'll buzz around this meadow
   in full morning glory.

I'm getting tired now
   and I think I'll rest
On that bull over there,
   on his fine, pointed horn.

I'm ready to leave—
   let all the world watch!
"Excuse me, Mr. Bull.
   You must be relieved
     to see me go."

"Why, no,"
   says the bull,
"I didn't notice you at all."

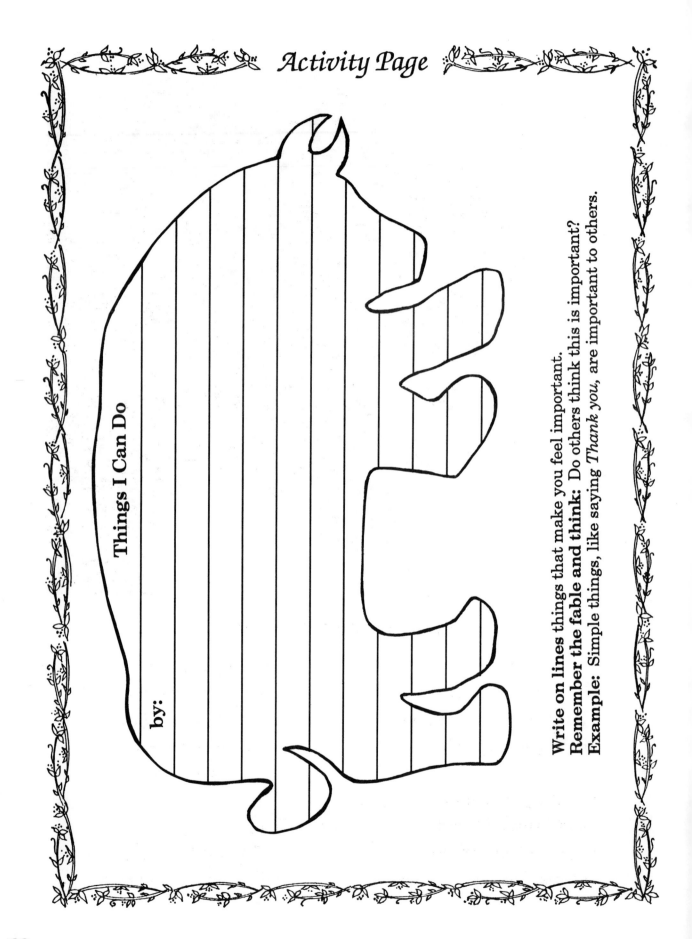

Things I Can Do

by:

Write on lines things that make you feel important.
Remember the fable and think: Do others think this is important?
Example: Simple things, like saying *Thank you*, are important to others.

Two Travelers and a Bear

Two boys, Tim and John, were walking through the woods. Suddenly a bear came out through some bushes.

Tim was fast and quickly climbed a tree.

John stood frozen and lost his chance to run away. He knew he couldn't fight the bear alone. So he fell to the ground and pretended to be dead. He had heard that bears usually won't touch a dead body.

The bear did as John had hoped. He strolled over, sniffed around John's head for a while, and then walked away.

When it seemed safe, John sat up. His friend, Tim, climbed down the tree and came to him.

"From the tree it looked like the bear was whispering in your ear," said Tim. "What did he tell you?"

John replied, "He told me not to walk with someone who would leave his friend in danger!"

What lesson can we learn?

*True friendship will help
when trouble comes.*

Tim was John's friend. He meant
no harm to John when he climbed
the tree. Tim had hoped that John
would run and climb a tree also.

Tim was happy to see the bear
only sniff at John, then walk away.

Later, John saw his chance to say,
in fun, that friends are supposed to
help each other when trouble comes.

Two Travelers and a Bear

Crash go the bushes,
   just to our right.
"A bear!" I cry, and my friend
   Tim is soon up a tree.

No time to run
   and surely
I can't fight this bear
   alone.

I know what I'll do.
   I'll play dead.
I've heard that bears
   don't touch dead things.

Ooooh, that tickles,
   Mr. Bear!
Your wet breath sends
   shivers down my neck.

I'm glad he's gone.
   I'll sit up now
And look for my friend
   who runs so fast.

"Hello," says Tim.
   "Are you okay?
It looked like that bear was
   telling you a secret!"

"You really want to know?" I say.
   "He told me not to walk
With someone who'd run
   when his friend is in danger!"

Start a "Friendship Club"

Pick a name:
 Example: Black Bears

Vote for:
 President
 Vice President
 Secretary

Memorize Motto:
 "True friendship will
   help when trouble comes"

Rules:
1 Be faithful
2 Be kind and considerate
3 Be helpful
4 Be truthful
5 Always share
   (Add rules that you want)

Badge

Make a badge:
Copy or trace a badge for each member.
To make badge thick, glue to cereal
  box first and then cut out badges.
Pick club colors and color the badges.
Pin a badge on each member.

Doing things as a club:
Decide on a time to meet—
  suggest one day each week.
Do things for each other and with
  each other.

You've just begun—and there's so much
that you can do together!

26

Retell the Fables
with
Finger Puppets

Copy or trace.
Cut out.
Tape sides at bottom.
Slide over fingers
and
retell
the story!

The Rabbit and the Turtle

from
Volume I

A Bell for the Cat

More Finger Puppets . . .

or

Cut or trace shapes and
tape to popsicle sticks
to make Stick Puppets.

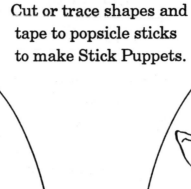

The Fox and the Crow

from
Volume II

The Fox Without a Tail

Glue figures to wood shapes
and display on your bookshelf.

The Town Mouse and the Country Mouse

from
Volume III

The Young Goat and the Wolf

Land of Aesop – II

Color Design by: _____

Date: _____   Age: _____

My Notes